ATLAS
OF THE
WORLD
STICKER BOOK

Contents

IMAGE CREDITS
Map illustrations: Daniel Limon (Beehive Illustration); Arpad Olbey (Beehive Illustration); Dreamstime.com; Shutterstock.

Photographs: (Dreamstime.com) 6t Ron Sumners; 6b William Milner; 7t Walter Arce; 7b Byelikova; 10t Batuque; 10b Lockstock;11t Filipe Frazao;11b Lisastrachan;14t Shuo Wang; 14b Matt Jacques;15t Steve Forney; 15b Minyun Zhou;18t Nightman 1965;18b Christian Delbert;19t Calin-andrei Stan;19b Sebastiangh; 22t Putatushkina; 22b Per Björkdahl; 23t Sigurdur William Brynjarsson; 23b Glen Vermeesch; 26t Vladimir Zapletin; 26b Alexander Melnikov; 27t Vvkuz62; 27b Michal Knitl; 30t Aleksandr Frolov; 30b Saiko3p; 31t Johan Bernspång; 31b Gao Qing; 34t Sergey Uryadnikov; 34b Sculpies; 35t Wrangel; 35b Ulldellebre; 38t Shanecycles; 38b Volodymyr Byrdyak; 39t Neil Burton; 39b Melissa Schalke; 42t Sophiejames; 42b Nickolayv; 43t Emicristea; 46t Rozenn Leard; 46b Danemo; 47t Tommy Schultz; 47b Awcnz62; (Shutterstock) 43b SeraphP.

The world is an astonishing place! Journey around it in this interactive sticker atlas.

Atlas of the World Sticker Book features colourful maps, more than **150 stickers** and fascinating facts about the amazing planet we live on. Discover awesome animals, marvellous monuments, natural phenomenons and much more as you explore the wonders of the natural and human world around you! As you travel through these pages, you'll discover answers to a host of questions, such as:

- What caused a massive crater in the US desert in Arizona?
- Where can you see the stunning Greater Bird of Paradise?
- Why is Namibia's coast in Africa called the 'Skeleton Coast'?
- Where in the world can you stay in a hotel made of ice?

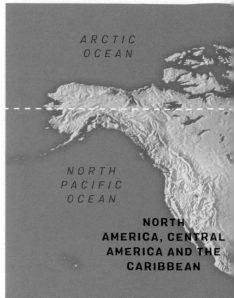

ARCTIC OCEAN

NORTH PACIFIC OCEAN

NORTH AMERICA, CENTRAL AMERICA AND THE CARIBBEAN

In this book, the world is divided into 11 regions, as shown on this world map. Each region is illustrated with a more detailed map and follow-on fact pages.

HOW TO USE THIS BOOK

Find the matching stickers for all the icons in the sticker pages and place them where marked on the 11 maps in the book.

The follow-on pages give extra facts about a selection of countries and tell the fascinating stories behind their icons.

At the end of the book there is a fun quiz to test your newly earned world-explorer skills.

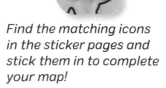

Find the matching icons in the sticker pages and stick them in to complete your map!

Icons show features and landmarks.

Please note the letters 'CE' next to a year stands for 'Common Era', the years after the reported birth of Christ. 'BCE' stands for 'Before Common Era'.

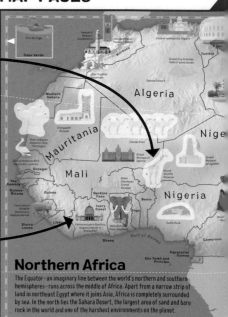

MAP PAGES

Northern Africa

The Equator—an imaginary line between the world's northern and southern hemispheres—runs across the middle of Africa. Apart from a narrow strip of land in northeast Egypt where it joins Asia, Africa is completely surrounded by sea. In the north lies the Sahara Desert, the largest area of sand and bare rock in the world and one of the harshest environments on the planet.

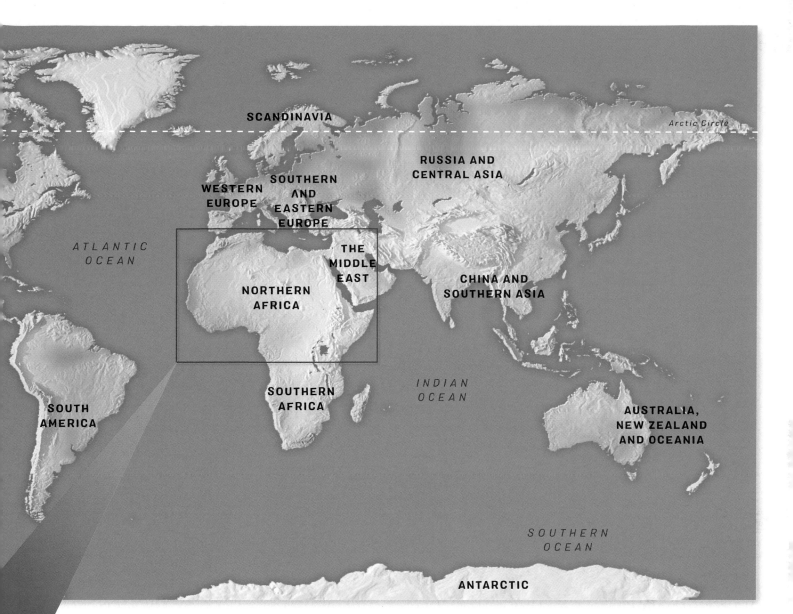

SCANDINAVIA

Arctic Circle

RUSSIA AND CENTRAL ASIA

WESTERN EUROPE

SOUTHERN AND EASTERN EUROPE

THE MIDDLE EAST

ATLANTIC OCEAN

NORTHERN AFRICA

CHINA AND SOUTHERN ASIA

INDIAN OCEAN

SOUTH AMERICA

SOUTHERN AFRICA

AUSTRALIA, NEW ZEALAND AND OCEANIA

SOUTHERN OCEAN

ANTARCTIC

FACT PAGES

Maps illustrate different inhabited regions of the world.

More fun facts about some of the key sights and features within each region.

Photographs provide real images of animals, major landmarks and other key features from each region.

North America, Central America and the Caribbean

Most of the continent of North America is covered by just two large countries – Canada and the United States of America. To the south lie Mexico and the small countries of Central America, and in the sea to the east are the many islands of the Caribbean. The continent includes coastal plains, deserts, great lakes and a climate that varies from arctic cold in the north to tropical heat in the south. Vast mountain ranges, such as the Rocky Mountains, run along the west of the continent and large areas of prairie and grassland stretch from the Gulf of Mexico right up to the Canadian Arctic.

Iceberg

Polar bear

Greenland

Walrus

Baffin Bay

Inuit person and dog sled

Moose

ARCTIC OCEAN

Beaufort Sea

Totem pole

Beluga whale

United States of America (Alaska)

Arctic Circle

Kodiak bear

Oil rig

DIRECT HIT

WHAT: METEOR CRATER

WHERE: ARIZONA, USA

Thousands of meteors collide with Earth every year. Most burn up as shooting stars, but a few actually reach the ground, and these are known as meteorites.

About 50 000 years ago, a very large meteorite slammed into Earth and made Meteor Crater.

Meteor Crater is about 167 m (550 ft) deep and 1.2 km (4000 ft) across.

Meteor Crater is one of the best-preserved meteorite craters on the planet.

DAY OF THE DEAD

WHAT: DAY OF THE DEAD FESTIVAL

WHERE: MEXICO

Don't be afraid of *El Día de los Muertos*, which is Spanish for 'The Day of the Dead'. This Mexican festival is a happy celebration in which people remember family and friends who have died.

People dress up as skeletons, paint their faces so they look like skulls and walk in colourful parades. The festival is famous for its model skulls painted in bright colours. Some smaller skulls are made from sugar, and can be eaten.

About eight hurricanes blow across the Caribbean each year. October is the worst month for these massive storms.

Brightly coloured skulls are often used to decorate houses to celebrate the Day of the Dead festival.

South America

South America is a continent of great contrasts. The hot tropical rainforest of the north gives way to lush Pampas grassland in the centre and the east, and in the far south is the cold, icy landscape of Patagonia. Passing through seven countries along the western edge of the continent are the Andes Mountains, which run almost the complete length of South America.

ATLANTIC OCEAN

Equator

Giant tortoise

Galápagos Islands (Ecuador)

Saint Vincent & The Grenadines

Barbados

Grenada

Tobago

Trinidad

Venezuela

Angel Falls, world's highest waterfall

Spectacled bear

Colombia

Guyana

Suriname

French Guiana

Amazon rain forest

Amazon River

Cocoa production, for making chocolate

Coffee-producing region

Cathedral of Brasília

Howler monkey

Scarlet macaw

Three-toed sloth

Brazil

Ecuador

Peru

Andes Mountains

Machu Picchu, ancient Inca city

Nazca Lines, massive ancient drawings in the desert sand

Lake Titicaca, boat made from reeds

Bolivia

Oruro Carnival, brightly dressed dancers

Copacabana Beach

Tropic of Capricorn

Christ the Redeemer statue, Rio de Janeiro

Green turtle

Container ship

Oil tanker

SOUTH ATLANTIC OCEAN

N E S W

South Georgia and South Sandwich Islands

Hand of the Rising Giant beach sculpture, Punta del Este

Iguazu Falls

Gran Chaco, armadillo

Paraguay

Uruguay

Palacio de los López, Asunción

Pampas, fertile grassy plains

Córdoba Cathedral

Commerson's dolphin

Falkland Islands (Islas Malvinas)

Magellanic penguin

Yungas Road, world's most dangerous road

Ischigualasto, rock formation

Ojos del Salado, world's highest active volcano

Argentina

Llama

Chile

Andes Mountains

Mount Fitz Roy, highest mountain in Patagonia region

Easter Island statues

Easter Island (Chile)

Andean Condor, national bird of Chile

Southern right whale

SOUTH PACIFIC OCEAN

South America

South America has some of the greatest natural wonders on the planet, and some of the most spectacular ruins from vanished civilisations. Scientists from around the world study its rivers, forests, deserts, glaciers, volcanoes and wildlife, and tourists trek for hours to reach the places where ancient people once lived.

Armadillos are the only mammals in the world whose bodies are covered with hard plates set into their skin.

LITTLE ARMOURED ONE

WHAT: ARMADILLO

WHERE: MUCH OF SOUTH AMERICA

An animal living in South America is covered from head to toe in hard, bony plates. This is the armadillo, which is Spanish for 'little armoured one'. It comes out mainly at night, moving slowly around, hunting for insects, worms and carrion (dead animals). If attacked, some types of armadillo curl up into a ball for protection.

LOST CITY OF THE INCAS

WHAT: MACHU PICCHU

WHERE: PERU

High up in the Andes Mountains in Peru are the ruins of Machu Picchu. It was a city built by the Inca people over 550 years ago. Toward the end of the 1500s, Machu Picchu was abandoned, but it is still a mystery as to why.

After that, its buildings fell into ruin and trees grew among them. Machu Picchu was lost from sight until it was rediscovered in 1911. As the trees were cleared away, the world began to find out about the 'Lost City of the Incas'.

Machu Picchu had a population of about 1000 Inca people.

The bare-throated bellbird of Paraguay is one of the world's loudest birds. Its call sounds like a hammer bashing on metal and can be heard over 1.6 km (up to 1 mile) away!

MIGHTY RIVER AND FOREST

WHAT: THE AMAZON RIVER AND RAINFOREST

WHERE: BRAZIL, PERU, BOLIVIA, COLOMBIA, VENEZUELA, SURINAME, ECUADOR, GUYANA, FRENCH GUIANA

The Amazon River is the greatest river in South America, and the world's second longest river, after the River Nile in Africa. From the Andes Mountains of Peru, it flows east for at least 6400 km (4000 miles), until it reaches the Atlantic Ocean.

The Amazon travels through the world's largest rainforest, where millions of trees produce about 20 per cent of the world's oxygen. This is why the Amazon rainforest is known as the 'lungs of the planet'.

More than 2000 different kinds of fish live in the Amazon River, including piranhas and electric eels.

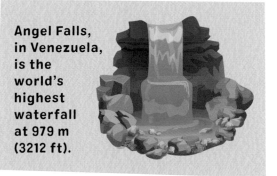
Angel Falls, in Venezuela, is the world's highest waterfall at 979 m (3212 ft).

No one knows for sure how the massive 82-tonne (90-ton) moai statues were transported across Easter Island for up to 18 km (11 miles) without the use of wheels, cranes or large animals.

The statues stand with their backs to the sea, staring out across Easter Island.

ISLAND OF STATUES

WHAT: EASTER ISLAND STATUES

WHERE: EASTER ISLAND (RAPA NUI)

Scattered across a tiny island, far out in the Pacific Ocean off the coast of South America, are hundreds of massive stone statues. These are the famous 'moai' of Easter Island.

A group of Polynesians, the Rapa Nui, somehow managed to sail in canoes to the remote island, which is 1770 km (1100 miles) from the nearest land. There, they established a distinct culture, carving the enormous moai between the 10th and 16th centuries.

Western Europe

Western Europe is a region of large islands (Britain, Ireland, Sicily and several others) and peninsulas that jut out into the surrounding seas. From the rugged cliffs and arctic winds of the Scottish highlands to the sun-baked mountains of Spain, Western Europe's landscape is varied. This includes the jagged, snow-capped peaks of the Alps mountain range, which stretch in an arc between France and Austria. In southern Italy, near to the warmer waters of the Mediterranean Sea, there are active volcanoes.

NORTH
ATLANTIC
OCEAN

Fishing trawler

Container ship

Giant's Causeway

Ireland

Rock of Cashel

Celtic
Sea

Irish Sea

Caenarfon Castle

Stonehenge stone circle

Buckingham Palace, London

United Kingdom

Angel of the North

Legend of Loch Ness Monster

Oil rig

Firth of Forth (Forth Rail Bridge)

North Sea

Ferry

Windmill

Keukenhof, flower garden, Lisse

Atomium, Brussels

Netherlands

Brandenburg Gate, Berlin

Germany

Engl

Western Europe

Millions of people visit the countries of Western Europe every year. Some are attracted by the natural beauty of the region, while others visit its famous cities, museums, art galleries and ancient ruins.

LANDMARK TOWER

WHAT: EIFFEL TOWER

WHERE: PARIS, FRANCE

The Eiffel Tower is named after Gustave Eiffel, the engineer whose company designed and built it. The iron tower took two years to build, and was opened in 1889 as the entrance arch to the World's Fair, a big exhibition. It was supposed to be taken down after 20 years, but by then the Eiffel Tower had become a symbol of France and was too important to lose. It is visited by over seven million people per year (that's almost 20,000 people a day!).

The Eiffel Tower is 324 m (1063 ft) tall. For 41 years it held the record as the world's tallest structure.

Construction of the Sagrada Família in Barcelona, Spain, began in 1882 and is still not complete today! It was designed by the world-famous artist Antoni Gaudi.

Stonehenge is set within in a vast, ancient landscape where there are several hundred burial mounds.

GREAT STONE CIRCLE

WHAT: STONEHENGE

WHERE: WILTSHIRE COUNTY, UK

Across the UK are more than 1000 ancient circles made from large upright stones. Stonehenge was made by prehistoric people more than 4000 years ago, who lined it up with the movement of the Sun. On the shortest day of the year (21 December), the Sun sets behind the tallest stone. There is a theory that the entire structure was a complex prehistoric calendar that counted the individual days in a year.

Stonehenge also acted as a lunar calendar, allowing a developing agricultural society to plan for the seasons of the year.

HIGHEST MOUNTAINS

WHAT: THE ALPS

WHERE: FRANCE, ITALY, SWITZERLAND

The Alps are the largest mountain range in Europe; the range stretches for about 1200 km (750 miles) across several countries. They are formed where two parts of the Earth's surface come together, pushing up the rocks between them to make the mountains. More than 100 mountains in the Alps are higher than 4000 m (13 000 ft). The highest of all is Mont Blanc, which rises to 4808 m (15 774 ft).

The Alpine marmot, a species of squirrel, is found throughout the European Alps. They can live at high altitudes and dig into very hard soil.

The highest mountains in the Alps are covered in snow all year round.

Venice, Italy, is a city built on more than 100 islands, with canals between them.

For almost 400 years, gladiator fights occurred at the Colosseum.

CRUEL COLOSSEUM

WHAT: COLOSSEUM

WHERE: ROME, ITALY

The Colosseum was built by the Romans and opened in the year 80 CE. It was an arena where 50 000 people gathered to watch gladiator fights and animal hunts. Gladiators fought with swords, spears, tridents and nets. Some wore body armour for protection.

When a gladiator fell, the crowd called out whether he should be allowed to live or die. It sounds horrific to us – but to the ancient Romans a gladiator show was their idea of a good day out!

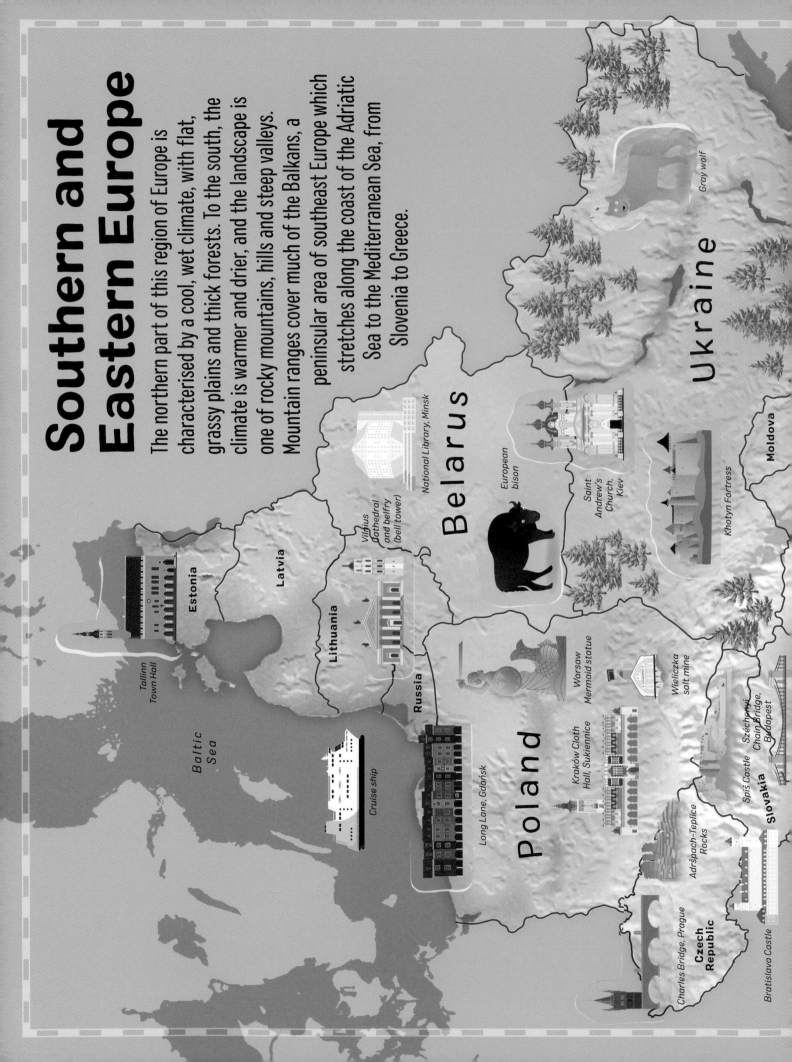

Southern and Eastern Europe

The northern part of this region of Europe is characterised by a cool, wet climate, with flat, grassy plains and thick forests. To the south, the climate is warmer and drier, and the landscape is one of rocky mountains, hills and steep valleys. Mountain ranges cover much of the Balkans, a peninsular area of southeast Europe which stretches along the coast of the Adriatic Sea to the Mediterranean Sea, from Slovenia to Greece.

Tallinn Town Hall

Estonia

Latvia

Baltic Sea

Vilnius Cathedral and belfry (bell tower)

Lithuania

Russia

Cruise ship

National Library, Minsk

Belarus

European bison

Saint Andrew's Church, Kiev

Khotyn Fortress

Ukraine

Gray wolf

Moldova

Long Lane, Gdańsk

Warsaw Mermaid statue

Kraków Cloth Hall, Sukiennice

Wieliczka salt mine

Poland

Adršpach-Teplice Rocks

Charles Bridge, Prague

Czech Republic

Spiš Castle

Slovakia

Bratislava Castle

Széchenyi Chain Bridge, Budapest

Black Sea

Cruise ship

Black Sea
mud bathing

Cyprus

Mediterranean Sea

Romania

Hungary

Varna Cathedral

The Acropolis
and Parthenon,
Athens

Aegean Sea

Bran Castle,
"Dracula's Castle"

Pelican,
Danube River

Belogradchik
Fortress

Bulgaria

Palace of Knossos

Greece

Serbia

TFYR
Macedonia

Crete

Ancient Theater
of Epidaurus

Cathedral of Saint
Sava, Belgrade

Cruiseboat,
Danube River

Croatia

Skanderbeg
monument,
Tirana

Albania

Olympia,
site of first
Olympic
Games

Bielolasica
Ski Resort

Bosnia and
Herzegovina

Avaz Twist Tower,
Sarajevo

Stari Most
Mostar

Montenegro

Ionian
Sea

Slovenia

Predjama Castle

Pula
amphitheater

Adriatic Sea

N
W   E
S

Southern and Eastern Europe

Southern and Eastern Europe are regions known for their rugged mountain terrain, forests and the Danube River – the second longest river in Europe, after the Volga. It's the birthplace of democracy and the Olympic Games, the location of the world's worst nuclear accident, and the home of the cruel prince who inspired Count Dracula.

DIGGING FOR SALT

WHAT: SALT MINE

WHERE: WIELICZKA, POLAND

Millions of years ago, southern Poland was covered by the sea. Over time, the sea dried up and a deep deposit of good-quality salt was left behind.

The best salt came from Wieliczka, where it was mined for hundreds of years. The salt miners left behind a vast network of tunnels and massive caverns, which visitors can now explore. More than one million people visit the salt mine every year.

Life-sized models show how miners worked in the Wieliczka salt mine.

The *qeleshe* is a traditional white felt cap worn by men in Albania, Kosovo, and the Albanian-speaking parts of Montenegro, Greece and TFYR Macedonia.

ANCIENT GREEK TEMPLE

WHAT: PARTHENON TEMPLE

WHERE: ATHENS, GREECE

The ancient Greeks built temples dedicated to their gods. The greatest temple was built in Athens, for the goddess Athena Parthenos. The temple became known as the Parthenon, after her.

Inside the Parthenon was a large statue of the goddess and a festival was held every four years in her honour. A grand procession of people went to the Parthenon to pay their respects to Athena.

The Parthenon was built 2500 years ago, on a high hill overlooking Athens.

The Olympic Games began at Olympia, Greece, in 776 BCE. The first modern Olympic Games were held in Athens in 1896.

PELICANS OF THE DANUBE

WHAT: WHITE PELICANS

WHERE: DANUBE DELTA (ROMANIA, UKRAINE)

The Danube River flows east through central and eastern Europe. As it nears the Black Sea and the end of its long journey, it forms a large area of marshy land called a delta. Every spring, about 2500 pairs of white pelicans arrive there from Egypt. They stay for six months to raise their young, before flying back to north Africa for the winter.

The Danube River is home to 300 species of birds. These include millions of pelicans who arrive every spring to raise their young.

Pripyat is a ghost (deserted) town in Ukraine. It was evacuated on April 27, 1986, the day after the nearby Chernobyl nuclear power plant exploded.

THE REAL COUNT DRACULA

WHAT: STATUE OF VLAD THE IMPALER

WHERE: ROMANIA

The novel of the blood-sucking Count Dracula – a vampire – has thrilled people for more than 100 years. But did you know that the author, Bram Stoker, based his character on a real person? He was Prince Vlad of Walachia. Prince Vlad was feared for his cruelty, and he was known as 'Vlad the Impaler' because he impaled his enemies on wooden stakes. He was also called 'Dracula', from the Romanian word *drac,* meaning 'devil'.

Vlad the Impaler (1431–76) is a national hero in Romania, because he fought the country's enemies.

Bran Castle in Romania is commonly known as 'Dracula's Castle', although it has no link with the real Prince Vlad. It just looks spooky!

Scandinavia

Scandinavia is the northernmost part of Europe. It includes Iceland, Europe's second largest island after Britain. The northern part of Scandinavia is within the Arctic Circle, where snow blankets the ground for much of the year. The rugged western side, along the coast of Norway, is indented by long, deep inlets of water called fjords. Large areas of Norway, Sweden, and Finland are covered in forests, while Iceland is almost treeless.

N
E
S
W

Polar bear

Spitsbergen

Global seed vault

Svalbard (Norway)

Barents Sea

Arctic Circle

Largest forested area in Europe

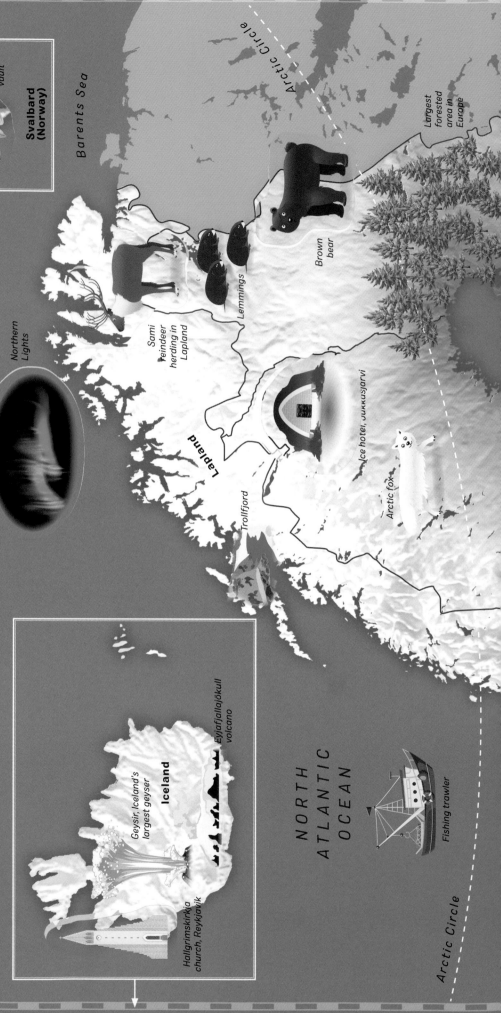

Northern Lights

Brown bear

Lemmings

Sami reindeer herding in Lapland

Lapland

Ice hotel, Jukkasjärvi

Arctic fox

Trollfjord

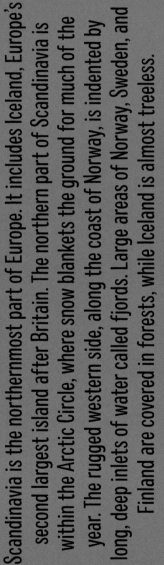

Geysir, Iceland's largest geyser

Iceland

Eyjafjallajökull volcano

Hallgrimskirkja church, Reykjavik

NORTH ATLANTIC OCEAN

Fishing trawler

Arctic Circle

Pujo tower, Kuopio

World's largest sauna, Kuopio

Finland

Helskinki Cathedral

Gulf of Finland

Gulf of Bothnia

Baltic Sea

Vasa warship

Viking longboat

Gray wolf

Sweden

Uppsala Cathedral

Drottningholm Palace

Poseidon statue, Gothenburg

Øresund Bridge

Little Mermaid statue, Copenhagen

Norway

Galdhøpiggen, highest mountain in Scandinavia

Ski jump, Lillehammer

Viking ship museum, Oslo

Ramnefjellsfossen, highest waterfall in Europe

Borgund Stave Church

Skagen lighthouse

Denmark

Hillerød (Frederiksborg Castle)

Oil rig

Norwegian Sea

North Sea

Scandinavia

The countries of Scandinavia have some of the world's most unspoilt and surprising landscapes. It's the homeland of the Vikings and where you can spend a night in a hotel made from ice. It's the place to see polar bears, reindeer and snow-covered lands, while the night sky above lights up with displays of dazzling colours.

REINDEER IN LAPLAND

WHAT: SAMI REINDEER HERDERS

WHERE: LAPLAND

Lapland is a large area of northern Scandinavia. It covers parts of Finland, Sweden, Norway and Russia. It's the home of the Sámi people, some of whom carry on the traditional way of life of reindeer herding. As spring approaches and the snow melts, reindeer move down from the mountains to lower ground. The Sámi people herd them and steer them toward their spring grazing grounds.

Before they began to use snowmobiles, the Sámi people travelled on sleighs pulled by reindeer.

The Vikings came from three Scandinavian countries: Denmark, Norway and Sweden.

BRIDGE, TRACK, AND TUNNEL

WHAT: ØRESUND BRIDGE

WHERE: ØRESUND STRAIT, BETWEEN DENMARK AND SWEDEN

The Øresund Bridge crosses a strait of water between Denmark and Sweden. It links the Danish capital Copenhagen and the Swedish city of Malmö. The bridge's upper level is a road and the lower level contains tracks for trains. It stretches out from Sweden for almost 8 km (4.9 miles) to an artificial island in the middle of the strait. On the island, there is an underwater tunnel to Denmark.

About 18 000 cars drive across the Øresund Bridge every day.

Green lights in the sky over Iceland are made by charged particles from the Sun interacting with gases in the atmosphere.

LIGHTS IN THE SKY

WHAT: NORTHERN LIGHTS OR AURORA BOREALIS

WHERE: NORWAY, FINLAND AND ICELAND

Spectacular displays of pink, green, yellow, blue and violet light are seen in the night skies above Norway, Finland and Iceland. These are the Northern Lights, also known as the Aurora Borealis. They are caused by particles from the Sun interacting with the Earth's atmosphere at the magnetic North Pole. This causes the air to light up in bands, or curtains, of colour.

Astronauts can often see the dazzling display of the Northern Lights from the International Space Station.

Iceland's Strokkur geyser erupts every few minutes to a height of around 30 m (100 ft). This is only half the height of Geysir, Iceland's largest geyser.

JET OF BOILING WATER

WHAT: GEYSERS

WHERE: HAUKADALUR VALLEY, ICELAND

Iceland has about 30 active volcanoes. It also has a lot of ice and water. When water seeps down into the ground and meets the hot volcanic rock, something amazing happens. The water is heated up until it is so hot it turns into steam. Under great pressure, it spurts up straight out of the ground, forming a natural jet of steam and boiling water, called a geyser (from an Icelandic word *geysa*, meaning 'to gush').

The *Vasa* warship sank in Stockholm harbour in 1628. It was raised in 1961, and is now a major tourist attraction.

Arctic Circle

Norwegian Sea

Barents Sea

Kara Sea

Kola Peninsula, world's deepest borehole

Severodvinsk, Russian navy submarine base

Reindeer herding by the Nenets people

Diamonds from Popigai impact crater

Church of the Savior on Spilled Blood, St Petersburg

St Basil's Cathedral, Moscow

Bolshoi Ballet, Moscow

Ural Mountains

Taiga forest

Russia

The Motherland Calls, a giant statue at Volgograd

Moscow to Vladivostok, Trans-Siberian Railway

Site of Tunguska event, a meteorite exploded above devastated a large area

Mount Elbrus, Europe's highest mountain

Georgia

Armenia

Caspian Sea

Baikonur Cosmodrome, world's largest spaceport

Aral Sea

Uzbekistan

Bayterek Observation Tower, Astana

Altai honey-producing bees

Kazakhstan

We Are Our Mountains monument, Stepanakert

Azerbaijan

Neutrality Monument, Ashgabat

Turkmenistan

Registan Square, Samarkand

Walnut forest, Arslanbob

Kyrgyzstan

Tajikistan

ARCTIC
OCEAN

Bering Strait

Chukchi Sea

Polar bear

East
Siberian
Sea

Siberia

N

W   E

S

Laptev
Sea

Arctic
loon

Volcanoes on
Kamchatka
Peninsula

Sea of
Okhotsk

Sika deer

Lake
Baikal,
world's
deepest
lake

Baikal
sturgeon

Siberian tiger

Tatarskiy Proliv

Russky Bridge,
Vladivostok, longest
cable-stayed bridge
in the world

Russia and Central Asia

Russia is a vast country that stretches across two continents, from Europe in the west to Asia in the east. The region of Siberia lies mostly within the Arctic Circle and its ground is frozen for much of the year. To the south are vast expanses of conifer forest, and beyond that are the mountains of northern Asia. South of Russia are the republics of Central Asia, such as Kazakhstan, with their vast treeless plains (steppes), mountain glaciers and abundant seas and lakes.

Russia and Central Asia

It's hard to comprehend the vastness of this part of the world. Russia is almost twice the size of the United States and has at least ten time zones. The region has also got a direct link to space, with the world's oldest and biggest space centre at Baikonur in Kazakhstan, where many space-exploration records have been set.

A Russian Soyuz rocket lifts off from Baikonur, on its journey into space.

GATEWAY TO SPACE

WHAT: BAIKONUR COSMODROME

WHERE: KAZAKHSTAN

The Baikonur Cosmodrome is the world's largest spaceport, launching satellites into space and rockets to the International Space Station. It was founded in 1955, and is operated by Russia on land that belongs to Kazakhstan. The spaceport has many firsts, including launching the first satellite, the first human into space, and the first piece of the International Space Station.

The Motherland Calls, in Volgograd, Russia, is Europe's tallest statue. Built to commemorate the Battle of Stalingrad (1942–43), it is 85 m (279 ft) tall.

WORLD'S LARGEST LAKE

WHAT: CASPIAN SEA

WHERE: KAZAKHSTAN, RUSSIA, AZERBAIJAN, TURKMENISTAN, IRAN

The Caspian Sea lies between Europe and Asia, and is the world's largest inland body of water. For this reason, it is known as the world's largest lake. It is about 1200 km (760 miles) in length, and is 480 km (300 miles) across at its widest point. It has many varieties of fish, including the sturgeon, which is caught for its meat and its caviar (fish eggs).

Sturgeon are found in the Caspian Sea and in Lake Baikal, which is a lake in eastern Siberia, Russia. Lake Baikal is the deepest lake in the world with a maximum depth of 1632 m (5354 ft).

The Caspian Sea is bigger than Germany, and just a little smaller than Japan.

WORLD'S LONGEST RAILWAY LINE

WHAT: TRANS-SIBERIAN RAILWAY

WHERE: RUSSIA

It takes about seven days for a train to travel the full length of the Trans-Siberian Railway, crossing almost the full width of Russia. The route runs between the capital Moscow and the port of Vladivostok in the east, covering a distance of 9289 km (5772 miles).

The railway crosses 16 major rivers and stops at 87 towns and cities. Every year, passenger trains carry millions of people, and freight trains transport coal, timber, machinery and other goods.

The Trans-Siberian Railway crosses through a variety of landscapes, including enormous pine forests – almost half of Russia is covered in trees.

Because of its great length, the Trans-Siberian Railway is nicknamed 'the backbone of Russia'.

There are only about 500 Siberian tigers living in the wild. It is an endangered species.

The Fedchenko Glacier is long and narrow and moves about 64 cm (26 in) per day.

SLIPPERY SLOPE

WHAT: FEDCHENKO GLACIER

WHERE: TAJIKISTAN

Glaciers are slow-moving masses of ice. They're found among the world's highest mountains, and around the North and South Poles. The mountainous country of Tajikistan has many glaciers: the Fedchenko Glacier is the world's longest glacier outside the polar regions, at about 70 km (45 miles) long. It gets its ice from several smaller glaciers, which merge into it.

Mongolia

Bactrian camel, Gobi Desert

Tiananmen, entrance to Forbidden City, Beijing

Bab-e-Khyber (Khyber Pass gate)

Afghanistan

Pakistan

Great Wall of China

China

Himalaya mountains

Tomb of Bibi Jawindi, Uch Sharif

Taj Mahal, Agra

Nepal

Mount Everest

Bhutan

Terracotta Army

Giant panda

Red Fort, New Delhi

Bandhavgarh National Park, Bengal tiger

India

Rice fields

Hong Kong

Myanmar

Vietnam

Bangladesh

Plain of Jars, ancient burial site

Laos

Arabian Sea

Golden Rock Pagoda

Thailand

Imperial City, Hue

Cambodia

Indian elephant

Marlin

Angkor Wat

South China Sea

Tea production

Bay of Bengal

Peninsular Malaysia

Sri Lanka

Phang Nga Bay

Petronas Towers, Kuala Lumpur

East Malaysia

Container ship

Indonesia

Singapore

Maldives

INDIAN OCEAN

Borobudur Temple, Java

China and Southern Asia

Asia is the largest continent, covering about one-third of the world's land surface. Pushing up along the border between China, Nepal and Bhutan are the Himalayas – the world's highest mountain range. They separate central Asia from India and southeast Asia. In the north of the region is the Gobi Desert, a vast expanse of bare rock across Mongolia. Along the desert edge are great dunes of sand, piled up high by swirling winds. Southeast of mainland Asia there are also several island groups, scattered across the Indian Ocean and the Pacific Ocean.

Cherry blossoms

Fugu fish

PACIFIC OCEAN

Juche Tower, Pyongyang

North Korea

Sea of Japan

Japan

High-speed Shinkansen train

South Korea

Seoul Tower, Seoul

Yellow Sea

Himeji Castle

East China Sea

Dragon boat

Philippines

Philippine Sea

PACIFIC OCEAN

Melanesia

Brunei

Celebes Sea

Indonesia

Orangutan

Coral Sea

China and Southern Asia

There are some amazing sights in this region of the world. From deep underground where thousands of pottery soldiers stand guarding an ancient tomb, to the world's highest mountain, it's an area of impressive buildings and stunning natural beauty.

ONE HUMP OR TWO?

WHAT: BACTRIAN CAMEL

WHERE: MONGOLIA, CHINA

Camels are the largest animals found in deserts. Those living in the hot, dry deserts of central Asia are called Bactrian camels, after Bactria, an old name for the region.

Unlike their one-humped cousins that are found in the deserts of the Middle East and North Africa, Bactrian camels have two humps on their backs. The humps contain stores of fat, which are a camel's emergency supplies. In times of hardship, the fat is converted to water and energy, keeping the camel alive.

Bactrian camels have shorter legs and are more heavily built than one-humped camels.

Camels have long eyelashes and ear hair, and nostrils that they can pinch shut to shield them from the sand blowing in the desert.

Mount Everest, Nepal, is the highest mountain in the world at 8848 m (29 029 ft).

IN THE FOOTSTEPS OF THE BUDDHA

WHAT: BOROBUDUR BUDDHIST TEMPLE

WHERE: JAVA, INDONESIA

There are more than 500 stone statues of Buddha at the temple of Borobudur. This explains its name, which means 'Temple of the Countless Buddhas'. It is the largest Buddhist monument in the world, built around 800 CE. Buddhist pilgrims slowly walk to the top of the building, following a long clockwise route. To Buddhists, the journey to the top represents the journey of life itself.

Borobudur is shaped like a stepped pyramid. On its circular platforms are 72 stupa (shrines), each containing a statue of the Buddha.

MAGNIFICENT CASTLE

WHAT: HIMEJI CASTLE

WHERE: HIMEJI, JAPAN

Himeji Castle is the largest and one of the most stunning castles in Japan. Building work began in the 1300s and it was added to and remodeled until the early 1600s.

Built mainly from wood and painted white, it is also known as the 'White Heron Castle'. This is because its many curved roofs remind people of this bird's wings.

The winding passages inside Himeji Castle were intended to confuse an invader.

According to legend, Himeji Castle is haunted by a ghost that appears nightly at one of its wells.

GUARDING THE EMPEROR

WHAT: TERRACOTTA ARMY

WHERE: CHINA

The tomb of Shi Huangdi, the first emperor of China, is guarded by an army. He died in 210 BCE, and thousands of life-sized figures of soldiers were buried with him. They were made from baked clay, known as terracotta.

In 1974, farmers digging a well discovered the Terracotta Army. Since then, archaeologists have unearthed more than 8000 terracotta soldiers and hundreds of chariots and horses.

The Terracotta Army has guarded the tomb of China's first emperor for more than 2000 years.

Angkor Wat, Cambodia, means 'City of Temples', and is home to hundreds of Buddhist temples.

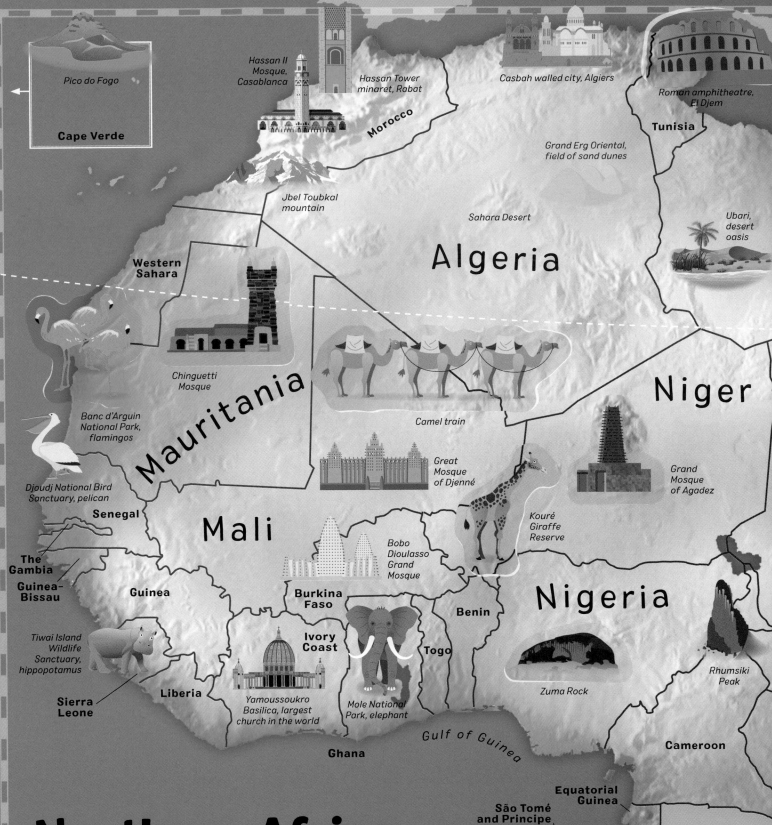

Pico do Fogo

Cape Verde

Hassan II Mosque, Casablanca

Hassan Tower minaret, Rabat

Casbah walled city, Algiers

Roman amphitheatre, El Djem

Morocco

Tunisia

Grand Erg Oriental, field of sand dunes

Jbel Toubkal mountain

Sahara Desert

Ubari, desert oasis

Western Sahara

Algeria

Niger

Chinguetti Mosque

Camel train

Banc d'Arguin National Park, flamingos

Mauritania

Grand Mosque of Agadez

Great Mosque of Djenné

Djoudj National Bird Sanctuary, pelican

Kouré Giraffe Reserve

Senegal

Mali

Bobo Dioulasso Grand Mosque

The Gambia

Nigeria

Guinea-Bissau

Guinea

Burkina Faso

Benin

Tiwai Island Wildlife Sanctuary, hippopotamus

Ivory Coast

Togo

Zuma Rock

Rhumsiki Peak

Sierra Leone

Liberia

Yamoussoukro Basilica, largest church in the world

Mole National Park, elephant

Gulf of Guinea

Cameroon

Ghana

Equatorial Guinea

São Tomé and Principe

Northern Africa

The Equator – an imaginary line between the world's northern and southern hemispheres – runs across the middle of Africa. Apart from a narrow strip of land in northeast Egypt where it joins Asia, Africa is completely surrounded by sea. In the north lies the Sahara Desert, the largest area of sand and bare rock in the world and one of the harshest environments on the planet.

Mediterranean Sea

Container ship

Suez Canal

Oil and gas fields

Pyramids, Giza

Libya

Egypt

Felucca, on
River Nile

Tropic of Cancer

Abu Simbel, ancient
Egyptian temple

Tibesti Mountains
(Toussidé volcanoes)

Red Sea

Chad

Sudan

Ancient Nubian
pyramids, Meroe

Eritrea

Zakouma National
Park, pangolin

Deriba Caldera,
volcanic crater

Fasil Ghebbi,
fortress city,
Gondar

Laas Geel,
cave paintings

Djibouti

Western
lowland
gorilla

Central
African
Republic

South
Sudan

Ethiopia

Somalia

Nechisar National Park,
crocodile

Equator

N

W   E

S

INDIAN
OCEAN

Northern Africa

From sandy desert in the north to tropical rainforest at the equator in the south, northern Africa is a land of great contrasts. It's also home to the world's longest river – the River Nile – along which the civilization of the Ancient Egyptians flourished. Their monuments were built thousands of years ago, but they are still a staggering sight today.

WESTERN LOWLAND GORILLA

WHAT: WESTERN LOWLAND GORILLA

WHERE: CAMEROON, CONGO, CENTRAL AFRICAN REPUBLIC, GABON, DEMOCRATIC REPUBLIC OF THE CONGO, GUINEA

Gorillas are the largest of the great apes (large primates) and are only found in Africa. The western lowland gorilla lives in the rainforests of central and western Africa. It can climb trees, but prefers to spend its time on the forest floor in family groups. It is an endangered species because it is hunted by poachers and its rainforest home is being destroyed.

The scientific name for the western lowland gorilla is *Gorilla gorilla gorilla*.

TOMBS OF THE PHARAOHS

WHAT: GIZA PYRAMIDS

WHERE: NEAR CAIRO, EGYPT

In the desert at Giza, Egypt, stands a group of three massive pyramids. Deep inside are the tombs of three of Ancient Egypt's early pharaohs (rulers).

The largest pyramid was built for pharaoh Khufu. Known as the Great Pyramid, it was built more than 4500 years ago using more than two million blocks of stone.

The other pyramids were constructed for Khufu's son, Khafre, and grandson, Menkaure.

Zuma Rock, Nigeria, is a massive dome-shaped rock in the middle of a flat landscape. It is 725 m (2400 ft) high.

The pyramids of the pharaohs Menkaure, Khafre and Khufu (left to right). Smaller pyramids are for members of their families.

'Sahara' is an Arabic word that means 'desert'.

People always think of the Sahara Desert as hot. But from December to February, temperatures at night can plunge often to freezing or below. Sand dunes can even be covered in snow.

WORLD'S LARGEST HOT DESERT

WHAT: SAHARA DESERT

WHERE: NORTH AFRICA

The Sahara is the world's largest hot desert. It covers most of

northern Africa, from Mauritania in the west to Egypt in the east – a distance of more than 5000 km (3100 miles). Deserts are areas that are barren, dry and hostile to life, and the biggest desert in the world is the Antarctic Desert, despite being much colder.

Only about ten per cent of the Sahara is sandy; the rest is gravel and rocky outcrops. The Sahara is getting bigger as grasslands along its southern border continue to dry up. In an attempt to stop this, trees and plants are being planted along the Sahara's southern edge. It's called the 'Great Green Wall of Africa'.

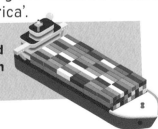

The Suez Canal, Egypt, was opened in 1869 and links the Mediterranean Sea and the Red Sea.

MOSQUE OF MUD

WHAT: GREAT MOSQUE OF DJENNÉ

WHERE: MALI

The Great Mosque of Djenné is the world's largest building made from sun-dried mud brick. The walls are covered in a thick layer of mud plaster. When it rains, the mud becomes soft and starts to wash away. For this reason, the mosque is given a new coat of mud every year. Hundreds of people mix mud into a sticky plaster, carry it in baskets up long ladders, then spread it on the walls with their hands to rebuild it.

Wooden posts stick out from the walls of the Great Mosque. They're ledges for workers to stand on when they're replastering the walls with mud.

Southern Africa

Much of the south and east of Africa is high, flat land, known as plateau country. The plateaus are bordered by mountains, or by lower-lying ground. Dense tropical rainforests cover the heart of Africa, particularly in Gabon, Congo, the Democratic Republic of the Congo and Uganda. There is high rainfall in this zone. South of the rainforests stretches the open grassy plains called the savannah, where many magnificent creatures like giraffes, elephants, lions, cheetahs and rhinoceroses roam.

Equator

Whale shark, world's largest fish

Kenya

Tea plantations

Maasai Mara people, shield and spears

Mount Kilimanjaro, highest mountain in Africa

Uganda

Nile perch, Lake Victoria

Tanzania

Serengeti National Park, lion

Rwanda

Burundi

Okapi Wildlife Reserve, okapi

Mountain gorilla

Zambia

Copper mines

Democratic Republic of the Congo

Congo

Kissama National Park, zebra

Gabon

Chimpanzee

Leatherback turtle

Oil rig

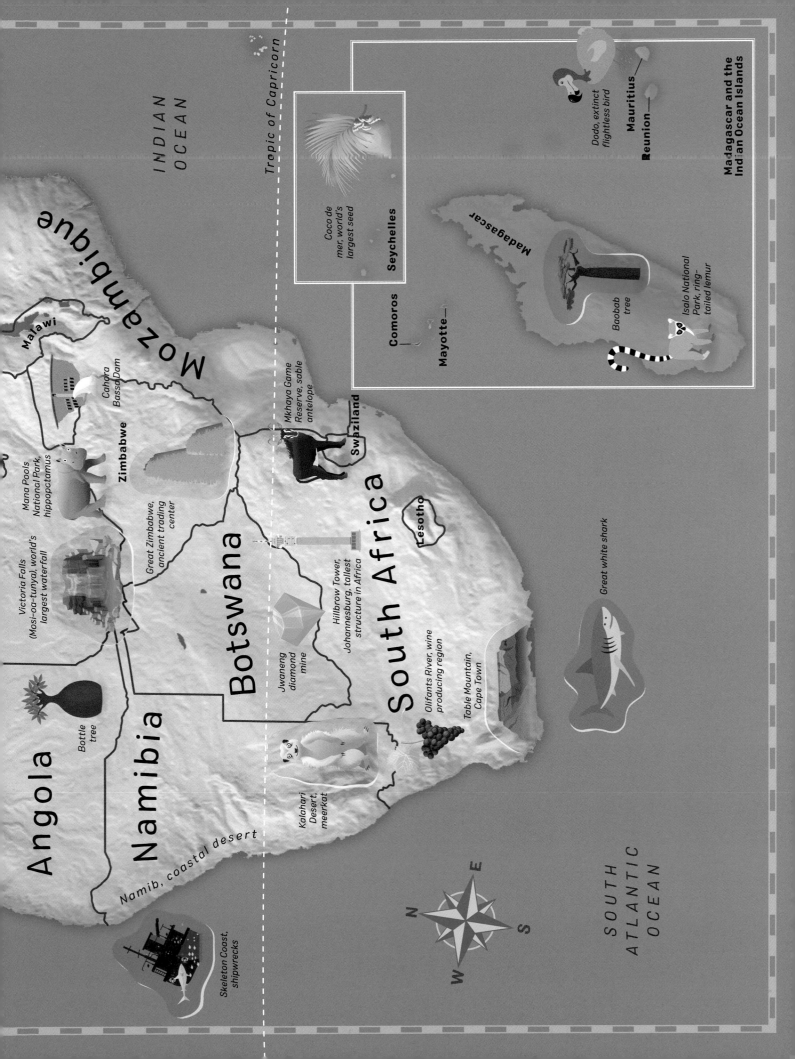

INDIAN OCEAN

Tropic of Capricorn

Coco de mer, world's largest seed

Seychelles

Comoros

Mayotte—

Dodo, extinct flightless bird

Mauritius

Reunion—

Madagascar and the Indian Ocean Islands

Madagascar

Baobab tree

Isalo National Park, ring-tailed lemur

Mozambique

Malawi

Cahora Bassa Dam

Zimbabwe

Mana Pools National Park, hippopotamus

Victoria Falls (Mosi-oa-tunya), world's largest waterfall

Great Zimbabwe, ancient trading center

Mkhaya Game Reserve, sable antelope

Swaziland

Botswana

Lesotho

Jwaneng diamond mine

Hillbrow Tower, Johannesburg, tallest structure in Africa

South Africa

Great white shark

Angola

Namibia

Bottle tree

Namib, coastal desert

Kalahari Desert, meerkat

Olifants River, wine producing region

Table Mountain, Cape Town

Skeleton Coast, shipwrecks

SOUTH ATLANTIC OCEAN

N E S W

Southern Africa

Africa's tallest mountain and the world's largest waterfall are among the natural wonders in this part of the great continent. It's also the homeland of some of the world's favourite wild animals, and the ruins of an ancient town that reveals past trade with faraway places.

HOUSES OF STONE

WHAT: GREAT ZIMBABWE

WHERE: ZIMBABWE

The ancient stone ruins of Great Zimbabwe were left by the Shona people. It was a trading centre, where goods were bought and sold.

At its height, in the 1300s, as many as 15 000 people may have lived there and in the surrounding countryside. For some unknown reason the town was abandoned by the 1450s, and it fell into ruin.

Stone walls and a tower at Great Zimbabwe. The word 'zimbabwe' means 'stone houses' in the Shona language.

Hundreds of animals and ships have been wrecked along the coast of Namibia, due to its strong currents and treacherous fog. This has led the coast to be called the 'Skeleton Coast'.

AFRICA'S TALLEST MOUNTAIN

WHAT: MOUNT KILIMANJARO

WHERE: TANZANIA

Standing 5895 m (19 341 ft) high, Mount Kilimanjaro is the tallest mountain in Africa. Every year, thousands of people climb Kilimanjaro. There are several routes and it takes a few days to get to the top, although altitude sickness prevents some from reaching the summit. The top is covered with snow and ice all year round, although not as much as there used to be. Some scientists say the snow and ice will have completely melted away in the next few years.

Mount Kilimanjaro is a dormant volcano that last erupted more than 300 000 years ago.

Large animals, such as antelopes and zebras, live largely in the national park and forests that surround Mount Kilimanjaro. They are rarely seen on the mountain's higher levels.

The falling water of Victoria Falls creates mist, through which rainbows can be seen.

At the top of Victoria Falls is the 'Devil's Pool', where adventurous swimmers splash about dangerously near the thundering waterfall.

SMOKE THAT THUNDERS

WHAT: VICTORIA FALLS

WHERE: ZIMBABWE–ZAMBIA BORDER

On the border of Zimbabwe and Zambia is the world's largest waterfall. In the language of local people it's called *Mosi-oa-tunya*, which means 'smoke that thunders'. In the English language, it is called Victoria Falls. It occurs at the place where the River Zambezi pours over a cliff, forming a giant curtain of water just over 1.7 km (1 mile) wide and 108 m (354 ft) high.

Table Mountain, South Africa, got its name because of its flat top.

LIONS OF AFRICA

WHAT: LIONS

WHERE: GRASSLAND, SOUTH OF THE SAHARA DESERT

Africa is known for its wildlife. Elephants, giraffes, zebras, rhinos and leopards roam the grassland in the east and south of the continent. This open countryside is called a 'savannah'.

Lions live in family groups called prides. These are made up of about 14–15 lions, of which at least two are adult males. The rest are females and their cubs. Most lions are found in Tanzania, especially in the Serengeti National Park.

A male lion and a female lioness. They are about the same size, but the mane of fur around the lion's face makes him look bigger.

Grand Bazaar, Istanbul

Wooden horse, Troy (Hisarlik)

Turkey

Rock towers, called "fairy chimneys," Cappadocia

Ancient stone heads, Nemrut Dagi

Mount Ararat

Caspian Sea

Syria

Iraq

North Cyprus

Cape Greco

Mediterranean Sea

Lebanon

Palestine

Umayyad Mosque, Damascus

Ishtar Gate, Babylon (Hillah)

Azadi Tower, Tehran

Persepolis, ancient Persian city

Kuwait Towers, Kuwait City

Dead Sea

Israel

Jordan

Ziggurat of Ur

Arabian oryx

Date palm

Kuwait

Persian Gulf

Bahrain

Great Mosque, Mecca

Oil well

Aspire Tower, Doha

Qatar

Arabian Desert

Dromedary camel

Red Sea

Saudi Arabia

Yemen

Dar al-Hajar, royal palace, Sana'a

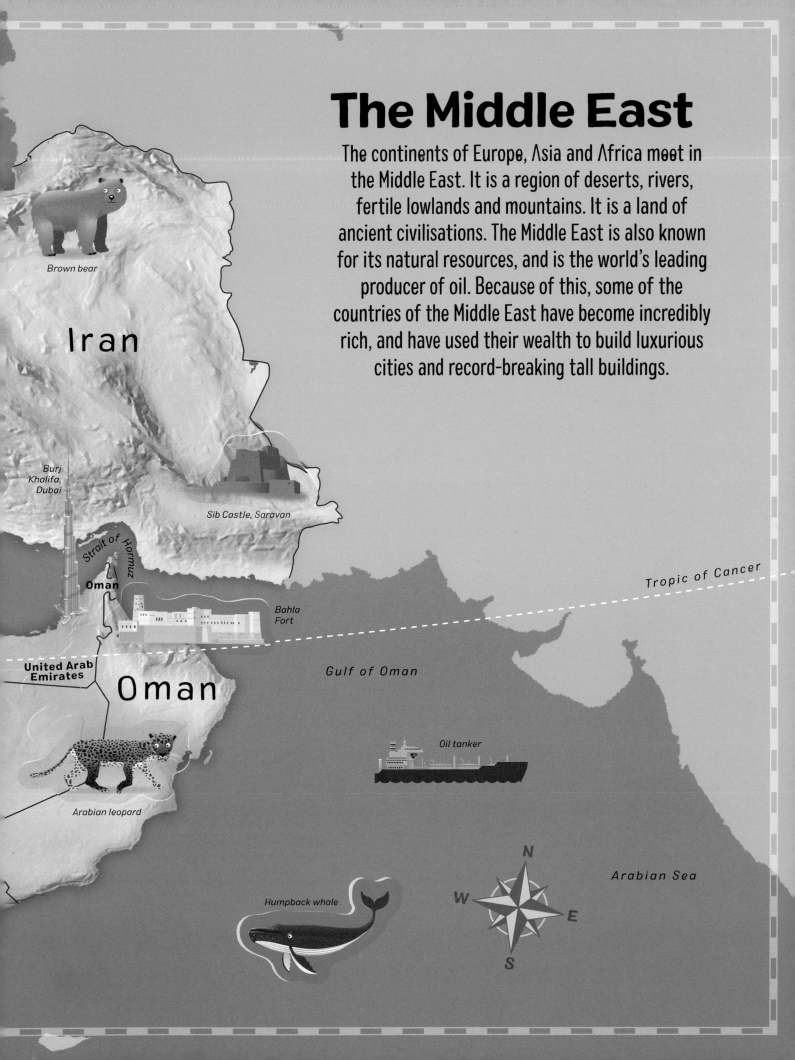

The Middle East

The continents of Europe, Asia and Africa meet in the Middle East. It is a region of deserts, rivers, fertile lowlands and mountains. It is a land of ancient civilisations. The Middle East is also known for its natural resources, and is the world's leading producer of oil. Because of this, some of the countries of the Middle East have become incredibly rich, and have used their wealth to build luxurious cities and record-breaking tall buildings.

Brown bear

Iran

Burj Khalifa, Dubai

Sib Castle, Saravan

Strait of Hormuz

Oman

Bahla Fort

Tropic of Cancer

United Arab Emirates

Oman

Gulf of Oman

Arabian leopard

Oil tanker

Humpback whale

Arabian Sea

N

W

E

S

The Middle East

The region is dominated by harsh desert landscapes and plants and creatures that have evolved to cope with these conditions. It's also home to the world's tallest building and some amazing natural features that have been turned into fantastic underground homes.

The outside of the Burj Khalifa is covered in a special cladding system to keep the tower cool in the hot summer weather.

TALLEST STRUCTURE

WHAT: BURJ KHALIFA

WHERE: DUBAI, UAE

Towering high above the Dubai skyline, the Burj Khalifa is the world's tallest human-made structure.

It is 838 m (2717 ft) tall and has 163 floors above ground and one floor below ground. To service these, 57 elevators take people up to offices, apartments, hotels and the world's highest outdoor observation platform on the 124th floor.

The Rub' al Khali in the Arabian Peninsula is the largest continuous sand desert in the world. The Sahara in northern Africa is a bigger desert, but it is mostly covered in rocks and gravel.

SUPER-SALTY SEA

WHAT: THE DEAD SEA

WHERE: ISRAEL

The lowest exposed land on Earth is found at the Dead Sea shore. The Dead Sea is actually a large salt lake that lies about 430 m (1400 ft) below sea level. The water in the lake is nearly ten times more salty than the world's oceans. This makes the lake and its shores too harsh a habitat for animals – that's why it's called the Dead Sea! Today, people use the salt in the lake to make cosmetics and as a natural medicine.

The Egyptian pharaoh Cleopatra believed the Dead Sea had mystical healing powers. While this may not be the case, minerals in the black mud and salts are beneficial for skin and joints.

Water evaporates from the Dead Sea, leaving behind large piles of salt crystals.

FAIRY CHIMNEYS AND CAVE CITIES

WHAT: ROCK FORMATIONS

WHERE: CAPPADOCIA, TURKEY

Known as 'hoodoos', these towers were formed when volcanic eruptions rained ash across the region millions of years ago. This ash formed into a porous, softer rock, which was covered by a harder layer of basalt. Gradually the softer rock eroded away, leaving a cap of hard basalt rock on top of pillars.

Cappadocia in Turkey is famed for this unusual landscape, beneath which are also a number of multi-level underground cities. These extraordinary settlements were carved out by ancient people, possibly as far back as 2500 BCE. They provided shelter for thousands of people and enabled them to hide from invaders.

The hard rock forms mushroom-shaped caps on top of the stony pillars.

DESERT ANTELOPE

WHAT: ARABIAN ORYX

WHERE: THE ARABIAN PENINSULA

These small antelopes have long, slender horns. In fact, some people believe that early stories about unicorns may have been caused by sightings of oryx that had lost one of their horns.

Hunting and habitat reduction almost saw this animal become extinct in the 1970s, but their numbers are starting to increase today.

Countries in the Middle East are responsible for about 30 per cent of the world's oil production.

The white coat of the oryx reflects the Sun's rays and its hooves are splayed and spade-like so it can walk on sand.

The Arabian oryx is the national symbol of Jordan, Oman, the UAE, Bahrain, and Qatar.

INDIAN
OCEAN

Arafura Sea

Timor Sea

Dolphin

Whale shark

Kakadu National Park,
estuarine crocodile

Emu

Australia

Royal Flying
Doctor Service,
air ambulance

Red kangaroo

Uluru

Kangaroo
crossing
sign

Swan River,
Perth

Wombat

Barossa Valley,
wine producing
region

N

W   E

S

Fremantle
Maritime
Museum

Great Australian Bight

Australia, New Zealand and Oceania

This vast area covers the island continent of Australia, as well as New Zealand and the many island groups of the Pacific Ocean. Scattered throughout the region's seas are more than 10 000 islands. The climate of this region is varied, from the wet, tropical conditions of the Pacific islands to the hot, dry deserts of central Australia and the glaciers of New Zealand.

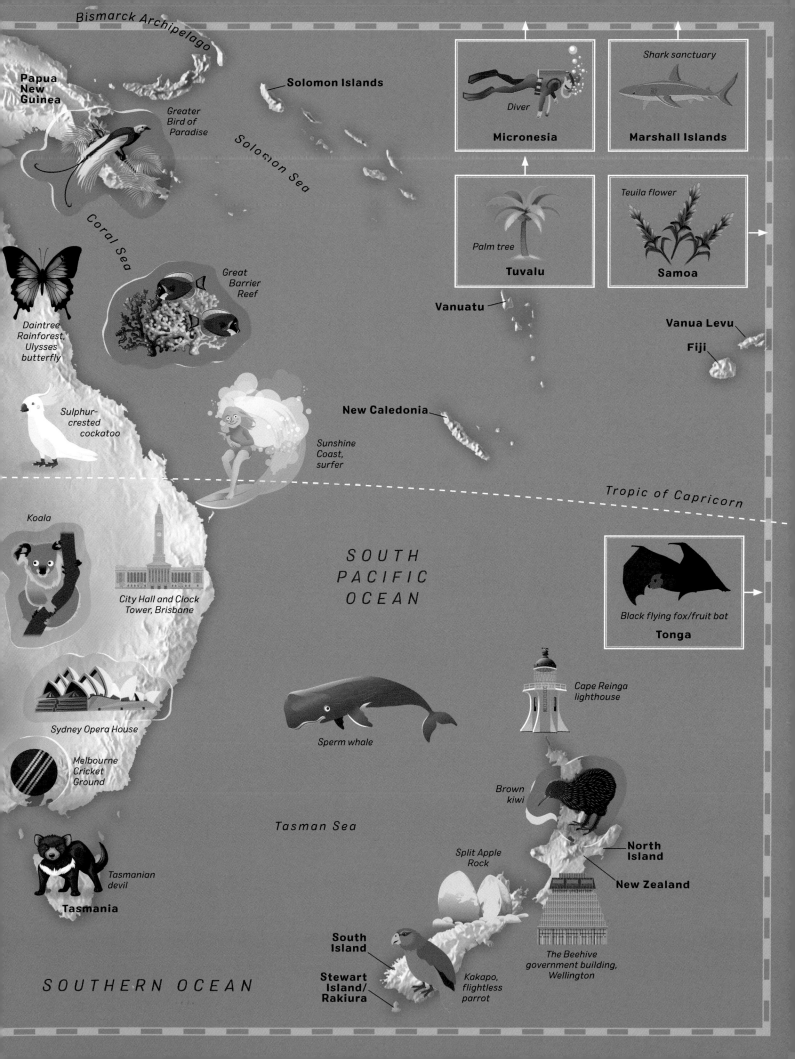

Bismarck Archipelago

Papua New Guinea

Greater Bird of Paradise

Solomon Islands

Solomon Sea

Coral Sea

Daintree Rainforest, Ulysses butterfly

Great Barrier Reef

Sulphur-crested cockatoo

Sunshine Coast, surfer

Diver

Micronesia

Shark sanctuary

Marshall Islands

Palm tree

Tuvalu

Teuila flower

Samoa

Vanuatu

Vanua Levu

Fiji

New Caledonia

Tropic of Capricorn

SOUTH PACIFIC OCEAN

Koala

City Hall and Clock Tower, Brisbane

Sydney Opera House

Melbourne Cricket Ground

Black flying fox/fruit bat

Tonga

Sperm whale

Cape Reinga lighthouse

Brown kiwi

Tasman Sea

Split Apple Rock

North Island

New Zealand

Tasmanian devil

Tasmania

South Island

Stewart Island/ Rakiura

Kakapo, flightless parrot

The Beehive government building, Wellington

SOUTHERN OCEAN

Australia, New Zealand and Oceania

Australia is the smallest of the world's continents but the largest island in the world. Tropical rainforests cover the far north, while much of the interior is a hot, dry desert. To the east and north of Australia is Oceania, which contains New Zealand and other western and central Pacific islands.

ROCK ART

WHAT: INDIGENOUS ART

WHERE: AUSTRALIA

Humans first arrived in Australia about 50 000 years ago. As the Indigenous Australian people spread through the huge territory they left behind ornate rock art. This took the form of rock paintings, dot paintings, carvings and rock engravings.

These paintings were made by spraying pigments over the artist's hands.

Near the centre of Australia is a huge sandstone rock formation known as Uluru. Uluru's rock glows red at dawn and dusk, and the local Indigenous people consider it a sacred place.

HOME, SWEET HOME

WHAT: TRADITIONAL HOUSES

WHERE: PAPUA NEW GUINEA

Traditional wooden houses in Papua New Guinea are built on stilts to protect them from flooding in the wet tropical climate. Typically, a whole family lives together in one large room. The fire used for cooking is also kept smouldering to ward off mosquitoes.

The roofs of traditional Papua New Guinea homes are made from thatched grass.

More than 140 species of marsupial are found in Australia. The largest is the red kangaroo, which can stand as tall as a person, at 1.8 m (6 ft).

UNDERWATER CITY

WHAT: GREAT BARRIER REEF

WHERE: AUSTRALIA

Lying just off the coast of north-eastern Australia, the Great Barrier Reef is the largest coral reef in the world. It is made up of more than 2500 different reefs and nearly 1000 islands, and stretches for about 2300 km (1400 miles).

This huge structure is made up of tiny animals called coral polyps, whose stony skeletons build up over thousands of years to create the chain of reefs, islands and atolls (coral islands).

The Great Barrier Reef is home to more than 1500 species of fish, including clownfish.

FLIGHTLESS BIRD

WHAT: KIWI

WHERE: NEW ZEALAND

This small, flightless bird is about the same size as a chicken, but is actually related to much bigger flightless birds like ostriches, emus and cassowaries. The females lay the largest eggs of any bird on the planet in relation to its size – the eggs can weigh as much as a quarter of an adult female.

The flightless emu is Australia's biggest bird. Each of its eyes has two eyelids: one for blinking and one to shield the eye from dust and sand.

Kiwis are usually nocturnal animals – they feed at night on worms, grubs and seeds.

Around the World Quiz

Now that you've been on this epic journey around the world, let's see what you've learned! See how many facts you can remember, or flip back through to find the answers before you check the solutions at the bottom of the page. You are now an ace world-explorer!

1 The Day of the Dead festival takes place in which country?

2 Which Pacific Island is famous for its stone statues?

3 Zuma Rock is in which African country?

4 In which country did the Olympic Games begin?

5 How high is Africa's tallest mountain, Mount Kilimanjaro?

6 Which two countries share the Niagara Falls?

7 What is the name of the world's largest rainforest?

8 The world's longest railway line crosses which country?

9 Two-humped (Bactrian) camels live in which continent?

10 Which is the world's largest continent?

11 In which country is the Great Pyramid?

12 Name two Scandinanvian countries ending in 'land'?

13 The Øresund Bridge links which two countries?

14 Where is Table Mountain?

15 The world's tallest building is in which city?

16 Which country does the kiwi bird come from?

17 What is another name for the Aurora Borealis?

18 Where can you find a huge sandstone rock formation known as Uluru?

19 Which Italian city is built on more than 100 islands?

20 Where is the Baikonur Cosmodrome?

Answers

1.Mexico 2.Easter Island 3.Nigeria 4.Greece 5.5895 m (19 341 ft) 6.Canada and the USA 7.The Amazon Rainforest 8.Russia 9.Central Asia 10.Asia 11.Egypt 12.Finland and Iceland 13.Denmark and Sweden 14.South Africa 15.Dubai 16.New Zealand 17.The Northern Lights 18.Australia 19.Venice 20.Kazakhstan